Ex Libris

Dedicated to Richard Curtis—friend and mentor

Many thanks to Avon Touring Theatre Company with
whom I spent several weeks learning about Boudicca.

Copyright © 1989 Tony Robinson
Illustrations © 1989 Andy Wagner
First published 1989 Blackie and Son Ltd

British Library Cataloguing in Publication Data

Robinson, Tony
Boodicaa and the Romans.
I. Title
823'.914 J

ISBN 0–216–92644–0

Blackie and Son Ltd
7 Leicester Place
London
WC2H 7BP

BOODICAA
AND THE
ROMANS

Tony Robinson

Illustrated by Andy Wagner

Blackie

Queen Boodicaa was in a stew, and I don't mean a bowlful of meat and gravy.

She was very, very cross.

'Don't do that!' she shouted to her daughter, Tracey, who was swinging from rafter to rafter with her eyes shut. 'It's dangerous, it leaves dirty finger marks and it disturbs the spiders.'

'And you can pack that in, too,' she yelled out of the window at her other daughter, Stacey.

Stacey was showing off. She was doing a handstand on the back of her horse with her eyes shut, and juggling two daggers and a fish with her feet while her horse trotted round the garden.

'But, Mum,' replied Stacey's upside-down voice, 'we want to be queens one day. We're only training.'

'Yes,' added Tracey, as she flew across the sitting room. 'Stop nagging!'

So Boodicaa picked up her crown and her lunch-box and went off on a picnic. She climbed the hill, spread out a table-cloth and ate a piece of celery and a hard-boiled egg.

Clunk! Dunk! Ber-donk! Up the hill came a Roman General followed by seventeen slaves with picks and shovels.

'You'll have to move,' ordered the General. 'We're going to build a road through here.'

'But we don't need a road,' replied the Queen. 'We've got a path.'

'The path is wiggly,' explained the General. 'The road will be nice and straight.' And he showed her the plans.

'I'm the British Queen,' said Boodicaa, screwing up the plans into a little ball. 'There will be no road.'

'I'm the Roman General,' replied the Roman General smoothing them out again. 'There *will* be a road – and what is more, it will be a big road, with crash barriers and service stations.'

'We'll hold a competition,' said Boodicaa. 'If you win, you can build your road. If I win, you can go away and never come back.'

'It's a deal,' said the General, and they shook on it.

Boodicaa called her tribe together.

'There's going to be a competition,' she announced, 'so I want you all to look smart.'

'Can we wear our war-paint?' asked the tribe.

'Good idea,' agreed the Queen. 'Bring out the woad!'

Tracey dragged out the big barrel of light-blue woad.

Stacey dragged out the vast vat of dark-blue woad, and the tribe began to paint themselves with it.

They painted their clothes with noughts and crosses,
their hair with blobs and streaks,
and their faces with flowers and snakes.

Then Boodicaa climbed into her chariot, the shiny brass one with big knives fixed to the middle of the wheels. No one messed with Boodicaa when she was in her chariot.

Out in the meadow the Roman General was waiting. Behind him were five Roman commandos with big muscles and squashed noses. At his feet were the slaves, chewing daisies.

Boodicaa rode up to him and stopped.

'Beyond the willow tree is the river,' said the General.
'Beyond the river is a marsh, and beyond the marsh is a
bell on a stick. The first person to ring the bell is the
winner. If it's a Roman, I win – if it's a Briton, you win.
1 – 2 – 3 – Go!'

And the five Roman commandos lumbered off.

'Off you go, Tracey,' said the Queen.

'All right,' answered Tracey. 'Just as soon as my
woad's dry.'

Clunk! Dunk! Ber-donk! The commandos clattered down
to the river.
Splash! Splosh! Splish! They waded through the water.
Slurp! Slurp! Slurp! They heaved their tired bodies
through the marsh.

'It's dry!' shouted Tracey and skipped down to the river,
leapt up into the air,
grabbed a branch of the willow tree,
swung across to the other side,
picked up a pebble
and hurled it at the bell on the far side of the marsh.

Ding! went the bell.

'We've won!' cheered the Britons.

'No you haven't,' snapped the General. 'That was a foul. You're not allowed to use stones.'

'What a bad loser!' said Boodicaa, but the General pretended not to notice. 'Round Two,' he announced.

'In this meadow are twenty roman coins. Whoever finds the most coins is the winner. 1 – 2 – 3 – Go!'

And the commandos lumbered off again.

'Off you go, Stacey,' said the Queen.

'All right, Mum,' answered Stacey, 'when I've finished this daisy chain.'

Clunk! Dunk! Ber-dunk! The commandos put on their glasses and started searching.

Crank! Dank! Ber-dank! They tripped over daisies and buttercups.

Clung! Dung! Ber-dung! They bumped into each other and fell over.

'I've finished it,' shouted Stacey and leapt on her horse,
tied her feet to the saddle,
swung underneath the horse's body,
and rode round the meadow picking up the coins in
her teeth.

Soon they were all standing in front of the General again.

'I got seventeen,' said Stacey. 'What's your score?'

'Three,' replied the commandos.

'We've won again,' shouted the Britons.

'No, it was a foul again,' snarled the General. 'You're not allowed to use horses.'

'Round Three,' said Boodicaa, 'and this time I'll decide the rules. The first person to tell a joke that makes the slaves laugh is the winner.'

'Erm ... erm ... erm,' went the commandos, but they didn't know any jokes.

'Oooh ... oooh ... oooh,' went the General, but he didn't even know what a joke was.

'My turn,' said Boodicaa. 'What's the difference between a Roman and a Briton?'

'We don't know,' chorused the slaves. 'What *is* the difference between a Roman and a Briton?'

'One likes a road that is boring and straight,
The other likes woad 'cos it makes him feel great!'

'Ha! Ha!' went the slaves. 'Hee! Hee! Ho! Ho! Ho! Ho!'
and they rolled about in the grass, slapped their sides and
tears of laughter poured down their faces.

It wasn't that funny, but the slaves didn't get
many laughs.

'We've won!' shouted the Britons for the third time.

'Yes, we certainly have,' agreed Boodicaa. 'General, do you promise not to build your road?'

'Yes,' said the General grumpily.

'And do you promise to go away?'

'Yes,' said the General even more grumpily.

'And never come back?'

'Yes,' said the General in a voice so grumpy it gave him a headache.

'And do you promise to keep your promise,' added Boodicaa, just to make sure.

'Yes,' said the General.

But he had his fingers crossed.